# CICADA OLYMPICS

## ENGAGING KIDS IN LIVE INSECT ACTIVITIES

SEA BUG

CINDY SMITH, PHD & RICHARD GROOVER, PHD

Photo credits for Cindy Smith, PhD; Gene Kritsky, PhD and Adria Bordas.

Illustrations by Brandon McPherson
www.brandondrawsfaces.com

Library of Congress Number: 2021907962

Publishers Cataloging-in-Publication Data
The Cicada Olympics: Engaging Kids in Live Insect Activities; by Cindy Smith, PhD & Richard Groover, PhD
62 pages cm.
Paperback ISBN: 978-1-7370933-0-5
Epub ISBN: 978-1-7370933-1-2

Printed in the United States of America

# Why we wrote this book

In spring of 2004, Dr. Cindy Smith was so incredibly excited that billions of Brood X cicadas were going to dig out of the soil and emerge in Northern Virginia that she created the Cicada Olympics event at Nokesville Elementary School in Nokesville, VA. (https://www.drcindysmith.com/cicada-olympics). In addition to introducing the 2nd grade class to these amazing insects, she also wanted each child to personally connect with their own cicada by naming it, designing a home for it, and having it participate in a series of events. Creating empathy for insects is one way to strengthen connections to the natural world. Many may fear these large insects because they emerge in the millions, sing a deafening song, fly clumsily into anything in their way, and stare unblinking with their beady red eyes. However, when one takes the time to get to know them personally, it is amazing what can be learned. When children worry more about their cicada's well-being rather than their own fear, they can view cicadas from a whole new perspective.

The first Cicada Olympics event was filled with laughing, cheering and a sense of accomplishment for the teachers, who were doubtful that an insect event could be so impactful. Kids, parents, volunteers, and teachers had a blast. Even 17 years later, grown-up students from that second-grade class tell Dr. Smith that the Cicada Olympics event was the most memorable, positive science activity they participated in during their whole K-12 career. Why? Because it was immersive and emotional. Concepts were reinforced, students felt ownership of their learning, and mostly, it was FUN! Learning experiences are memorable when they evoke emotions. At the Cicada Olympics, students overcame their fear of insects, experienced sheer excitement when cheering wildly for their own cicada athlete, and felt sadness when having to release their personal learning tool after the event.

In Chapter 1, you'll learn about overcoming fear when teaching with live insects. Chapter 2 jumps into the life cycle of the periodical Cicada and where to find them emerging. Chapter 3 explains how to set up and launch an event and Chapter 4 contains the activities for a successful event.

Looking for laughs?  Lots of silly jokes on selected pages!

Adult Cicada on lambs ear leaf © Cindy Smith, PhD

**The Coolest Science Activity I Ever Did**

The coolest science activity I ever did involved cicadas in 2nd grade. Professor Smith brought hundred of cicadas to my 2nd grade class and we got to go outside and play with them. We had cicada boat races which was really fun. I remember having a cicada crawl on me and being really scared at first, but towards the end I thought it was awesome. While I still hate a lot of bugs today, whenever the cicadas come every few years I always get excited to see them because of this day.

Comment from college student Coolest Activity Cicadas Second grade

Cindy teaches pre-lesson to second graders

Cicada examines large diamond ring © Cindy Smith, PhD

# Table of Contents

Nymph emergence holes in soil © Cindy Smith, PhD

Cicada nymph in tunnel © Gene Kritsky

Cicada nymphs in their tunnels wait to emerge with others at night crawling up any vertical surface.

Nymph left tunnel climbed thumb © Cindy Smith, PhD

Cicada Nymph Climbs Tire and Molts © Adria Bordas

What's the difference between a fly and a cicada? A cicada can fly, but a fly can't cicada.

6

# Chapter I

## Teaching with cicadas when you are terrified of bugs

### Insect Anxiety is Real

Many adults are afraid to look at, touch, or be near large, crawling critters. Even cicada exoskeletons, which are not alive, are terrifying to some people. This paralyzing fear of things that crawl is real, and it's called Entomophobia. Throughout this book, however, we'll simply refer to it as insect anxiety.

In Drs. Smith and Groover's 25 years of working with teachers and youth in both classroom and outdoor-based programming, they have watched kids pick up on and emulate the fears, worries, and anxieties of adults. For example, when a small child finds a beetle and excitedly shoves his hands into his teacher's face, facial expressions of fear and horror combined with an anxiety-induced verbal response like, "Oh my! Get that disgusting bug away from me and go wash your hands!" immediately communicates to the child that their discovery is unwanted, dirty, and disgusting. The likelihood of that child exploring outdoors and sharing another discovery is diminished. In the same way, angrily stomping a spider that runs across the floor while children are watching, directly communicates that spiders are meant to be killed. Even toddlers will yell out, "Kill bug!", when they see an insect scurrying across the playground. Children mimic what they see.

### Why show compassion to insects and spiders?

Modeling compassion for peers and all facets of our environment is important at all ages. When a child watches an adult capture a caterpillar or a spider and release it outside, they learn to have empathy. In the big picture, our planet is currently experiencing what researchers call an insect apocalypse. The numbers and diversity of insects world-wide is declining. For those who fear bugs, this may not seem alarming, but insects pollinate 30% of the fruits and vegetables that we eat, and bugs are a primary source of protein for most baby birds. Without these pollinators working hard in our fields and greenhouses, food prices will escalate, and bird populations will decline. As children are our future natural resource managers, teaching empathy for all creatures at a young age truly helps our planet.

## Why teaching with live insects is rewarding

As we teach learners of all ages, we repeatedly see that children who had multiple experiences with nature at a young age develop positive attitudes toward the environment as they become adults. Children who are introduced to insects and feel connected to natural or green spaces in the classroom or at home are more inquisitive about nature. Numerous studies have found learning in natural environments boosts academic performance, enhances critical thinking, and increases enthusiasm for learning.[1,2,3,4,5] Undergraduate elementary education majors in Dr. Smith's hands-on science courses routinely report that their most positive K-12 experiences with science occurred during an outdoor field trip.

What should you do when you see a low flying cicada? Duck.

Developing conversations about and positive relationships with nature is exactly what we need to raise a generation of youth ready to protect our planet.

1. Matsuoka, R.H., (2010). Student performance and high school landscapes: Examining the links. Landscape and Urban Planning, 97(4), 273-282.
2. D. Li and W. Sullivan. (2016). Impact of views to school landscapes on recovery from stress and mental fatigue. Landscape and Urban Planning. 148: 149-158.
3. Kuo, F.E., and A.F. Taylor. (2004). A Potential Natural Treatment for Attention-Deficit/Hyperactivity Disorder: Evidence From a National Study. American Journal of Public Health 94, 9:1580-1586.
4. Chawla, L., Keena, K., Pevec, I., Stanley, E., (2014). Green schoolyards as havens from stress and resources for resilience in childhood and adolescence. Health & Place, 28, 1-13.
5. Louv, R. (2006). Last child in the woods: Saving our children from nature-deficit disorder. Chapel Hill, NC: Algonquin Books of Chapel Hill.

In teacher workshops, most participants agree that watching live caterpillars metamorphosing into butterflies is a more effective learning and memorable experience than simply completing worksheets on insect life cycles. Teachers tell us they prefer vertebrates in the classroom, but students are open to anything that moves. Kids often tell us that they like that insects have eyes and personalities. They like that insects move, jump, fly, and do unexpected things, and many kids love insects so much that they wish that they could talk with them. Some teachers are a bit more skeptical of uncontained insect engagement, but in our experience, the memorable learning that occurs is worth the time investment in insect anxiety reduction.

During an outdoor schoolyard professional development workshop for elementary school teachers, Dr. Smith plucked an old crinkly cicada exoskeleton off a tree and showed it to the teachers who were sitting at picnic tables. A few stood up and backed away. Two screamed and climbed onto a picnic table. One even yelled, "I will NOT look at that bug!" and ran back inside the school. Dr. Smith calmly asked the teachers how they think their students view those sorts of interactions. Once everyone calmed down, the importance of positive facial expressions when teaching about nature was explained. We practiced the steps in our patented approach to calming insect anxiety while at the same time getting kids excited, even when they are terrified.

## Getting Your Game Face On

As former high school and collegiate athletes, Drs. Smith and Groover routinely prepared for game play using determined and intense facial expressions. Sometimes this was used to psych out opponents. At other times, this game face was used to build up our own confidence prior to the jump ball on the basketball court, or while sitting on the starting line at a rowing regatta.

Getting a game face on has also proven to be a very effective way for both parents and educators to confront their insect anxiety, promote insect empathy, and highlight discoveries with children.

 What do you call a Magicicada that can't sing? Female.

## Confronting Insect Anxiety when you are terrified.
When an excited child approaches you, insect in hand and says "Look what I found!"

**Practice these steps in advance...**
1. Take a deep breath and channel your inner scream into excitement by saying something like, "Wow! That's amazing."
2. While gently speaking to the child, place your hands lightly on the student's shoulders and slowly rotate them in the opposite direction, hiding the insect from your view. Without looking at the bug, take another deep breath and calmly say, "I would love it if you could show this to your classmates and teach them about your new insect friend."
3. Call other kids over to look. Have them focus on the discovery rather than your fear.
4. To keep the focus on the discovery, ask the child to point out the head, count the legs or wings and share how they found it. **Let them be the expert.** To reinforce empathy, remind the children that they are very big, and likely very scary to the insect, and thus they should ask their friends to be very gentle and speak quietly.
5. **Always honor discoveries**, as that will truly motivate other children to also seek out praise through their observations. Always ask children to release the insect exactly where they found it.

You may have adult helpers during your Cicada Olympics event who want to share how much they detest cicadas. To nip that in the bud, keep reminding them how excited everyone is about the incredible event and that their positivity will go a long way in building inquisitive minds.

## How to Engage those who are too scared to look
**Some children and adults will be too afraid to get too close to the insects.** You can help them better understand cicadas

by calmly asking them to help you find different things on the insects. For example, rather than saying something like, "Koby, look at this cicada!" ask a question like, "Koby, can you help me figure this out? Do you think the edges of this cicada's wings are orange or brown?"

In Dr. Smith's environmental education programs, targeted questions asking for help have been shown to move learners beyond their fear and into a place where they want to help you solve a problem. You can ask children to help you figure out what color the eyes are, and how many legs the cicada has. Comparison questions may also help calm their fear. "Does this cicada have long back legs for jumping like grasshoppers and crickets?" Cicadas do not have long back legs, so you can share that they are not likely to jump off of your hand. You can also ask questions like, "Why do you think cicadas have red eyes?" or "How far do you think they can fly?"

## Why asking questions and not knowing the 'right' answer is absolutely ok

**Do you have to know all the answers to these questions?** Nope.
**You do not need to have answers to questions or to explain observations.** On the contrary, ask the kids what they think. "What else did you notice?" "How do you think they hang on to tree bark?" Encourage them to share their ideas verbally with each other. Asking learners to explain more about their observation supports deeper reasoning, encourages them to support ideas with evidence and builds their confidence to ask even more questions...just like scientists and engineers.[6]

Asking children to look closely at how cicada nymphs hang onto fingers or trees teaches focused observation.
© Cindy Smith, PhD

6. National Research Council. 2012. A Framework for K-12 Science Education: Practices, Crosscutting Concepts, and Core Ideas. Washington, DC: The National Academies Press. https://doi.org/10.17226/13165.

Cicada molting on Yellowwood tree © Gene Kritsky, PhD

Molting Cicada wings filling more © Cindy Smith, PhD

Cicada nymphs molt, and wiggle out of their tight exoskeletons. Wings are small at first (top left), and slowly fill with fluid and extend (top right). Exoskeletons are left on trees and leaves after molting and are very easy to collect for activities.

Why do cicadas have exoskeletons? Because they would look silly if they wore sweaters.

Newly molted adult cicada wings filling © Cindy Smith, PhD

# Chapter 2
## All about Cicadas

### Types of Cicadas
**The Cicada Family and Relatives.**

Cicadas are a type of plant-sucking insects related to aphids, leaf-hoppers, and spittle bugs. They are classified as Hemipterans. Hemiptera is an order of insects that have pointed, straw-like mouths that they use to stab into plant stems and suck sap or xylem from them. Spittle-bugs, which look like little wads of spit along plant stems, are related to cicadas. These young nymphs cover themselves with bubbles for protection. Other cicada relatives are the leafhoppers, the small green bugs that resemble thorns with tiny legs along stems. Insects in this group are good at climbing and perching, but most are not talented jumpers like crickets or grasshoppers, because their hind legs are about the same size as their other legs. Cicadas do not have any pinchers, which makes them an excellent choice of insect for use in teaching.

There are more than 3000 types of cicadas world-wide, and they are **by far the best and loudest insect singers.** Most types of cicadas complete their life cycle from egg to nymph to adult in about 2 to 5 years with some living up to 21 years! Compared to mosquitos, which only live for a few months, or crickets that live for only one season, cicadas live incredibly long lives for insects. Most types of cicadas do not dig their way out of the ground all at once like the 17-year and 13-year periodical cicadas we will be working with in this book.

While living underground cicada nymphs feed on plant and tree roots. Their exoskeleton is like a shell, protecting their muscles and inner organs. As they grow larger, and a new exoskeleton is ready underneath, nymphs shed their outer exoskeleton in a process called molting.

Because most of a cicada's life is spent underground, humans rarely see the young white squishy nymphs. However, we do hear the adults singing away in the treetops during the summer.

## Annual Cicadas

Cicadas that live for 2 to 5 years are generally called annual cicadas because we see nymphs emerging from the ground every single spring and summer. They are great singers and more green than the darker black periodical Magicicadas. It is difficult to catch annual cicadas because they are much better flyers than periodical cicadas.

## Periodical Cicadas - the Magicicadas

Periodical cicadas are different from annual ones, in that billions of them emerge at once every 13 or 17 years. They are found in eastern North America and belong to the genus, *Magicicada*. There are seven species. Four of these seven species have 13-year life cycles, and three have 17-year cycles. Periodical Cicadas have talents that include living underground in the dark for years, molting, digging, tree climbing, and singing loud for all to hear. Adult cicadas are not good at running, jumping, flying, or hiding well from birds, dogs, foxes, coyotes, bears, or people.

All periodical cicadas of the same 13 or 17-year life cycle type that emerge in a given year are named together as a single "brood." While it can be confusing to non-cicada experts to name the groups like this, it helps everyone keep track of when to expect the next emergence. If you check the US Forest Service Map, it is possible to find adult periodical cicadas during late spring in almost any year if you travel to the right tree-filled location. They only emerge to the east of the Great Plains because that is where deciduous trees (trees that lose their leaves) are common and there is more rainfall.

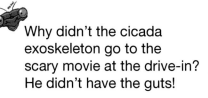

Why didn't the cicada exoskeleton go to the scary movie at the drive-in? He didn't have the guts!

# Where to Find Cicadas[1]

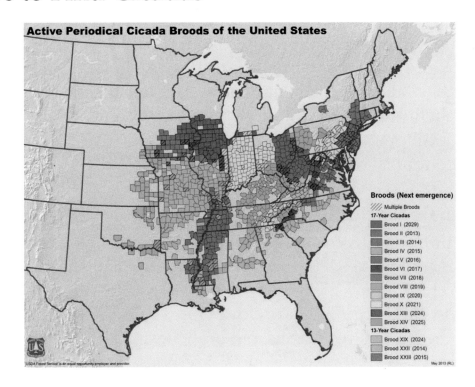

## Where are cicadas emerging?

The best place to find out if there will be a cicada emergence near you is to check the brood maps located on this U.S. Forest Service Map or at these websites: https://cicadas.uconn.edu/broods/

1. Liebhold, A.M., Michael J.B., and Rebecca L.L., "Active Periodical Cicada Broods of the United States," USDA Forest Service Research Station, Northeastern Area State and Private Forestry, map, 2013.

https://www.cicadamania.com/cicadas/where-will-17-13-year-periodical-cicadas-emerge-next/

## Why do cicadas stay underground for 17 years and then emerge at once?

Researchers believe that cicadas have evolved to having a 17 year childhood period as a way to avoid predators. Using their straw-like style, the nymphs feed on plant juices, grow and molt five different times underground. When the soil temperature reaches 64°F (18°C), usually in mid-May, they all dig their way out of the soil together, or within a couple of days of each other. Scientists think it is because there is safety in numbers. These slow-moving, clumsy flyers are easy prey for most any hungry bird or animal. If the emergence is huge, like for Brood X, there will be billions and billions of them in any one location. The likelihood that they all get eaten is quite low, because the predators' bellies are too full, and they cannot eat any more. Millions will survive and breed, and the cycle will continue.

## What animals eat cicadas?

Any birds that eat insects will eat periodical cicadas, but other predators include foxes, coyotes, bears, box turtles, snakes, raccoons, opossums, chipmunk, chickens, cats, and dogs. People will even cook them up and eat them. They are slow, clumsy flyers that are very easy to catch in the air. On tree trunks and branches, they remain in one spot and do not try to run away. Their shiny bodies with orange striped wings and bright red eyes make them quite easy to find. This is one reason they make excellent subjects for insect activities with kids.

## How do the nymphs know the exact day to start digging toward the surface?

This is a big question that is currently being studied. Nymphs grow and molt at different rates underground, but how they know to wait until it is the 13th or 17th year is unclear. Researchers like Dr. Chris

Simon at the University of Connecticut think
there has to be some sort of a molecular clock,
something in their genes that helps the cicada
nymphs count the years. Since they feed on juices of tree roots they can
likely tell when the seasons change above ground. Researchers rely on
the help of volunteers like you to report where you are seeing them, so
they can determine where the edge of the brood is located. We highly
encourage you to use the Cicada Safari app, to share cicada photos and
locations: https://cicadasafari.org/

What do you call a cicada that sings too much? Annoying.

## What does the emergence look like at first?

A few weeks before emerging in late spring, the nymphs of cicadas
dig exit tunnels to the surface. These small holes are about half an inch in
diameter (1.3 cm) and look like someone poked holes with an unsharp-
ened pencil. Sometimes, the nymphs build little mud chimneys, or "tur-
rets," over their holes. On the first night of emergence, nymphs leave
their burrows around sunset, walk toward a nearby plant or tree, climb
upward, and then begin their final molt to adulthood. Their brown exoskeleton cracks down the back and over the next few hours, the white
gushy adult backs out of its exoskeleton. It rocks, pulling its head, front
legs, wings and then finally its abdomen out of this shell. As the wings
extend, filling with fluid, the body color darkens from white to black.
Depending on temperature, it may take a few days for the new exoskeleton to fully harden. The old exoskeleton remains on the tree and the new
adult climbs higher to join the rocking Magicicada party in the treetops.

## What does the emergence look like after millions of cicadas have emerged?

The soil around the base of the deciduous trees will have hundreds,
if not thousands, of holes where nymphs emerge. Hundreds of brown
exoskeletons will be seen on tree trucks, shrubs, sides of houses, even
car tires. The cicadas will crawl up any plant or vertical surface nearby.
Cicadas will be flying clumsily through the air and crawling all over the
tree branches. If you look up, you'll see masses of small, black insect
bodies in the trees. What you will notice most is the singing. It will be
so LOUD that you will barely hear other people talking while outdoors.

## How do the male cicadas sing? What do their songs sound like?

About a week after emerging, the males begin singing while the nearby females watch and flick their wings in response. Males have ribbed small song organs called tymbals, which are sort of like drums with flexible ribs on top. Tymbals are located under their wings on the abdomen. To make noise they flex their muscles, which bends the ribs on their tymbals. Every time a rib on the tymbal bends or buckles, a click sound is made. The 'hums' that you hear in the trees are incredibly rapid bends in their tymbals. To mimic how this works, you can hold a bendy straw near your ear. Pull and bend the straw slowly, listen for the clicks each time the straw ribs are bent slowly. Next, bend the straw rapidly and listen. If you could bend the ribs so fast your hands were a blur, the clicks would run together and sound like the 'hum' you hear cicadas make when they sing. The female cicadas love this song and will flick their wings at males whose songs they enjoy.

We encourage you to play the songs of cicadas to your kids or students as they will likely recognize these iconic sounds of summer. While listening to the songs, close your eyes and imagine a tiny little tan membrane vibrating back and forth. At first you can hear the clicks, but as the males vibrate the tymbal faster it sounds like a continuous buzz. You can see images and listen to songs of annual and periodical cicadas on these sites:

https://www.cicadamania.com/cicadas/common-cicadas-of-north-america/ https://songsofinsects.com/cicadas

## Can I get the cicadas to sing to me?

Yes! With the right noisemaker, you can trick cicadas into thinking you are a singing cicada and possibly get them to sing to YOU. Cicadas are known to respond to lawn mower sounds, toy clickers, finger snaps, kazoos and even noisemakers often used at New Year's Eve celebrations. First, find a group of live cicadas. They can be outdoors on a tree, or you can try this with live male cicadas in a container. Watch them for about 1-2 minutes before you 'sing' to them.

Click your clicker rapidly at least 10 times in a row. Watch the cicadas. Do they seem to notice? Do they move toward your sound? Snap your fingers. Play different pitches on your kazoo. Do they react? You can also put your lips together like duck lips, fill your cheeks with air, and make the deepest sound you can while blowing out of your vibrating lips. Practice making a high-pitched vibrating sound as well. Watch and listen for the cicadas to talk back to you.

Why couldn't the cicada exoskeleton play music? She didn't have any organs (or tymbals)!

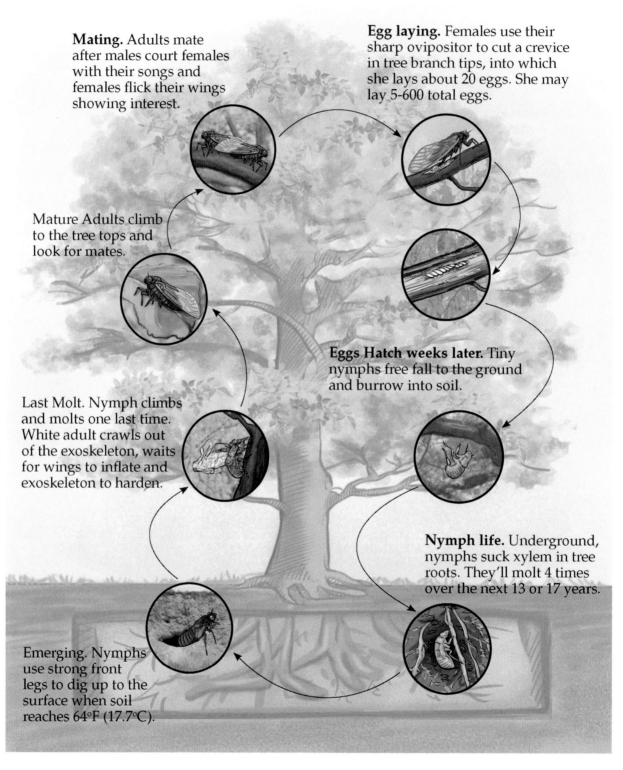

**Mating.** Adults mate after males court females with their songs and females flick their wings showing interest.

**Egg laying.** Females use their sharp ovipositor to cut a crevice in tree branch tips, into which she lays about 20 eggs. She may lay 5-600 total eggs.

Mature Adults climb to the tree tops and look for mates.

**Eggs Hatch weeks later.** Tiny nymphs free fall to the ground and burrow into soil.

**Last Molt.** Nymph climbs and molts one last time. White adult crawls out of the exoskeleton, waits for wings to inflate and exoskeleton to harden.

**Nymph life.** Underground, nymphs suck xylem in tree roots. They'll molt 4 times over the next 13 or 17 years.

**Emerging.** Nymphs use strong front legs to dig up to the surface when soil reaches 64°F (17.7°C).

What do you call a cicada floating in the creek? Bob.

## What is ovipositing?

Ovipositor

Each slit contains 20 -30 eggs

After mating, female cicadas lay 4-600 eggs, but not all in the same spot. They prefer the thin branches of oaks, maples, ash, elms, pear, and other fruit trees, but they will lay eggs in many tree types. When ready, the female will extend her sharp ovipositor, which looks like a thin black sword sticking out of her abdomen, and carve a groove in the branch. She will lay eggs in this groove.  The tiny nymphs hatch weeks later and drop to the ground where they burrow into the soil and spend 13 or 17 years feeding on plant juices, avoiding predators and living their lives until emergence. Adult periodical cicadas live only for a few weeks. By mid-July, all have disappeared.  The purpose of their short adult life is to reproduce. You will likely see the tips of tree branches where eggs were laid, flagging (flapping in the wind) with dead leaves.

Eggs are tiny! You can see egg images here: https://www.cicadamania. com/cicadas/category/cicada-anatomy/eggs/

Why is it better to be a cicada than a cricket? Because cicadas can play cricket but crickets can't play cicada!

What do you name a cicada with only 3 legs on one side? Eileen (I lean).

# Chapter 3

## How to Setup and Launch a Cicada Olympics Event

## Planning Your Event

10 Steps to deliver an incredibly fun learning experience.

1. Find out where and when the periodical cicadas are likely to be emerging
2. Get your team excited - this can include only your class, but it is much more fun in a crowd
3. Select the date
4. Select activities
5. Invite volunteers
6. Gather supplies
7. Send home a parent/guardian letter (a suggested letter is included in this eBook)
8. Schedule Pre-lessons to get kids excited! Teach them how to do cicada calls and wing flips. Encourage students to decorate cicada houses.
9. Gather cicadas and exoskeletons prior to the event
10. Day of event – how to set up stations – each activity in Chapter 4 will have the instructions listed.

### 1.   Where Can I Find Hundreds of Magicicadas?

Periodical cicada emergences have been accurately documented for many years, and thus are quite predictable. You can see the years, locations and expected emergence dates for each Brood listed here: https://www.cicadamania.com/cicadas/where-will-17-13-year-periodical-cicadas-emerge-next/

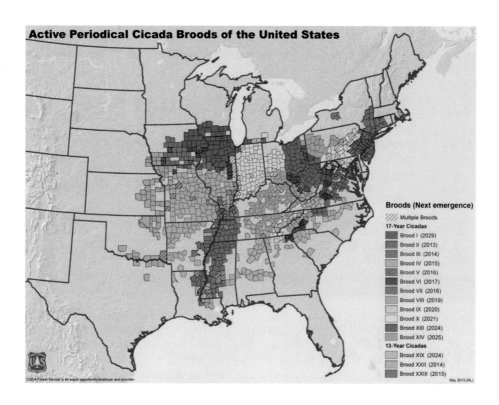

## 2.    Generate Excitement with your team

As soon as possible, meet with your school, neighborhood, friends, and teaching team to share your idea and why it will be such a fun event. You'll probably get a little push back from teammates who are a bit wary of insects, so make sure to share some of the observation, math, science, and art skills children can practice through this authentic learning experience. If they are nervous, let them know they do not have to touch the cicadas (more on this in Chapter 1). Integrating these live, slow-moving superstars into your event not only reinforces learning objectives, but more importantly it encourages kids to become experts on cicadas.  This authentic event teaches learners to ask questions, explore, and discuss their natural world.  Insect empathy, a skill often omitted in early education, is incredibly important now more than ever, as many types of insects, including pollinators of our food crops, are in serious decline globally.

What is tan, squishy and spends its whole childhood sucking on tree roots underground? A cicada.

### 3.    Scheduling Date of your Cicada Olympics event

The best way to select a date is to check the brood emergence maps for your area. Periodical cicadas emerge when the soil temp reaches 64°F at 8 inches deep (which is 17.8°C at 20cm deep). At the time of this book publication, we find the website, cicadamania.com, which is maintained by leading cicada researchers, to be the most up to date resource with maps and reporting on emergence times. https://www.cicadamania.com/cicadas/where-will-17-13-year-periodical-cicadas-emerge-next/

Select a time that is mid-way through the predicted emergence month. For example, if cicadas are predicted to emerge in Mid-May, you may want to plan your event one to two weeks later. But keep in mind, insects do not listen to website predictions and may emerge earlier or later depending on the soil temperature.

### 4.    Select Your Cicada Olympics activities

In addition to the pre-lesson cicada introduction, we have a collection of 13 activities in this book. Select the number of activities you'll have at your event and decide whether you want kids to visit each activity station or if they will self-select to visit stations of interest.

If you want to make a passport of events that you would like your child or children to participate in, it can be as simple as the one shown here. At each station kids can receive a stamp, check mark, or hole punch when they are done.

> **Cicada Olympics Passport**
>
> ❏ Measuring with Cicadas
> ❏ Magnifying Cicadas
> ❏ Building Pyramids
> ❏ Cicada Boat Race
> ❏ Cicada Car Race
> ❏ Cicada Math
> ❏ 3D Cicadas
> ❏ Cicada Sketching

### 5.    Invite and Gather Volunteers

To run a smooth in-person event, we recommend one adult or older youth to manage each activity station. These leaders need no experience, just general guidance in how to ask engaging questions. Send an exciting note out to your parents, guardians, friends and neighbors inviting them to join you as volunteers AND to share the excitement about this incredible event using live learning tools. Below is an example:

# CICADA OLYMPICS

*Dear Parents and Guardians,*

*As you may have heard, the periodical cicadas are emerging. On ___ (date),we are hosting the Cicada Olympics in this area: _____ from ____ (time) to ____ (time). During this authentic learning experience, children have the opportunity to visit up to 13 different learning and playing stations. While working with insects may sound a bit kooky, we assure you that this will be an exciting, memorable, and terrific learning experience for all of the children... and even the adults! Bring your cameras!*

*We are looking for up to ____ (#) volunteers to help with this event. All supplies and instructions will be provided. _____ (teacher) will meet with volunteers beforehand at ___ (time) in ____ (place) to go over individual station activities and expectations for this fun event. Volunteers will run one station and repeat the same activity with each new group of kids that comes your way. If you are unable to join us, you can help by getting your child excited for this rare occurrence at home by watching cicada videos or reading about cicadas together. Please return this note if you are interested in joining the fun and learning. More information will be sent home as we get closer to the date of the Cicada Olympics.*

*Thank you very much for your support. I look forward to an awesome day!*

*Sincerely,*

- - - - - - - - - - - - - - -

*Child's name* _____ *Child's teacher* _____

*Volunteer's name* _____

*____ I DO wish to volunteer ____ I am NOT able to help, but I wish I could!*

# 6. Order and Gather Supplies

Create your activity list, **compile the number of recommended supplies you will need at each station to support the number of students you will be hosting.** Below is an example:

## Cicada Olympics Stations

| Activity | Materials Needed |
|---|---|
| **Make a Cicada House** | • Chinese food take out boxes, cleaned milk or juice cartons, yogurt cups<br>• Stamps to decorate if desired<br>• Hole punches for popping air holes<br>• Pipe cleaners to use as carrying handle if using milk cartons<br>• Markers for writing child and cicada names on houses |
| **Select Your Cicada** | • Mesh butterfly enclosure or large box containing enough live cicadas for each child to have one.<br>• Recommend collecting 2 live cicadas per child, as some may fly away |
| **Cicada Boat Races** | • Kids bring in boats from home or constructed in class<br>• Kiddie pool or large storage bin that can be filled with water<br>• Pieces of cardboard, about 8.5 x 11 that kids can use to fan the boats<br>• 4-8 sticks and string for lane lines<br>• Duct tape to attach sticks to each end<br>• Clipboard with kids' names, with space for the cicadas' names and the place they finish (if you keep score)<br>• Pencils for scorekeeper |
| **Cicada Car Races** | • Ramps and cars supplied by the school or neighborhood<br>• Kids can bring cars in as an option<br>• Clipboard with paper with kids' names and space for the place they finish<br>• Pencils for scorekeeper |
| **Measuring with Cicadas** | • At least 6-10 objects to measure<br>• 5 Exoskeletons and/or slow-moving adult cicadas in clear cup with lid<br>• Pencils and/or dry erase markers<br>• Measuring with Cicadas worksheets, 1 per student<br>• If using laminated worksheets, supply dry erase markers and wipes |

| Counting with Cicadas (older kids) | • Math worksheets, one per child<br>• Pencils<br>• Answer key for station leader |
|---|---|
| Cicadas under Magnification | • Field microscope (if available) or magnifiers<br>• 6 Expired cicada specimens glued or taped (double-sided tape) to white index cards: Cicada adult showing the back side, Cicada adult showing the back side the underside, Cicada adult male, and a female, and 2 exoskeletons<br>• Worksheets- 1 per child with questions about observing cicadas |
| Cicada Sketching | • Templates printed, 1 per child<br>• Markers/colored pencils or crayons. Make sure to have red for eyes<br>• Some cicadas for reference and inspiration |
| 3D Cicadas | • Printed templates for kids to cut, or pre-cut cicada body parts (head, eyes, body, wings, legs) for kids to glue<br>• Glue sticks<br>• Scissors, if parts are not pre-cut<br>• Finished 3D cicada model |
| Building pyramids with cicada exoskeletons | • Platforms, at least 16in x 16in, made out of poster board or thick cardboard (one platform for each class or team)<br>• Glue (At least 1 bottle per team)<br>• 100s of Exoskeletons. The more you have, the taller the pyramid (be sure to provide MANY exoskeletons)<br>• A demonstration model – exoskeletons glued to make a pyramid or recognizable shape like a person, dog, etc… |
| Guess the number of cicada exoskeletons in the jar | • Jar full of exoskeletons<br>• Small cards for kids to write their names and guesses<br>• Empty box with a slit cut into it for students to place their guesses<br>• Pencils |
| Cicada Life Cycle | • A cardboard cut-out or a laminated image of an oak tree<br>• Circular cut-outs of the life cycle phases |
| Cicada Gems | • Card stock printed with The Cicada Olympics, cut into small squares,<br>• At least one exoskeleton per child, more recommended as they're fragile<br>• Metallic gold or silver spray paint<br>• Liquid glue to attach exoskeletons to card stock |

7. **Send home the Parent/guardian/neighbor letter** including instructions for Cicada Boat Race Engineering Challenge. Below is an example

*Dear Parents, Guardians or Neighbors,*

*On ___(date) we will be participating in the first ever Cicada Olympics. The children will be engaging in all sorts of fun activities on the playground including drawing cicadas, making cicada houses, guessing the number of exoskeletons in a jar, racing cicada boats and more! Each child will have a live cicada to carry with them to all the events.*

*If you live in an area that is experiencing a cicada emergence, please bring in any and all live cicadas or exoskeletons that you can. The _____ classes will be competing to see which class can build the biggest exoskeleton pyramid.*

*All students will create their own boat at home (or together ahead of time if possible) and bring it with them to the event. We will race boats in a kiddie pool or large plastic tub on the playground.*

## Cicada Boat Race Rules:

- All boats must be 8 inches long (20 cm) **or shorter** and no more than 4 inches (10cm) wide. Boats should be open on top so the cicada captain will be visible.

What is a cicada's favorite musical instrument? A tymbal!

- Boats can be built out of *any material* (sticks, leaves, wood, foil, plastic, paper, cardboard, water bottle, etc...). Boats will be moved by the wind, so creating a sail-like structure to catch the wind will be helpful.
- If you want to use an existing boat, such as a toy boat, **you must modify it in some way to make it your own creation** (Ex: turn it into a sailboat).
- To make sure your boat floats, test it at home before bringing it to the event.
- When the live cicada boat captain is placed in the boat, the crowd must be able to see the cicada and it must be able to move around the boat.

Please join us for this fun filled event, even if bugs scare you. Parents don't have to touch the cicadas. It is much more fun to investigate these periodical cicadas than to worry about them. Authentic learning leads to great questions and critical thinking skills. Bring your camera!

## 8.   Schedule Pre-Lesson to get youth excited

We recommend having a pre-meeting with the children to build excitement and alleviate stress for those kids that may be afraid of insects. During this 20-30 min period, share a bit about periodical cicadas with kids in your classrooms, homes, museum or on your website. These can be in-person, virtual or with pre-recorded videos. You can use the script below.

## Pre-lesson/Cicada Introduction

The speaker should wear a jacket or layer they can peel off to demonstrate molting. To create sound-making tymbals, cut out two tan, rounded rectangles, (approximately 6 x 5 inches or 15 x 13 cm) with a few horizontal lines on them and tape them to your hips. Below is a script you can use to engage. Script in italic is what you *do* while you are speaking.

a. *Show an image of a 17 year cicada and ask kids to tell you the color of the body (black), eyes (red) and wings (clear with orange bands).* Cicadas have a head *(touch your head)*, a thorax *(touch your chest)* and abdomen *(hands on your belly and hips)*. These rectangles are the tymbals, the sound-making organs on males.

b. For 17 years the little cicada nymphs have been living under the soil in the dark. Their favorite, and only, food is juice that they suck from tree roots. Their mouth is made up of a sharp straw that they stab into small tree roots and then suck the juice. Yum! *Make an O with your lips, place a straw in your mouth and smile.* They cannot bite you because they only have a straw for their mouth.

c. When the temperature rises to 64 degrees underground, the nymphs get restless. *Squat down very low, wriggle a bit, look up and start to dig upwards in the air with your hands. Slowly reach your full standing.* Ahhh… I see the sun! *Have the kids do the same, but then start wiggling.* My skin is too tight, and I feel something on my back. *Whisper:* "I hope I get my big wings." *Say:* "When cicadas grow bigger they have to molt. What do they do?" *Molt! Slowly peel your jacket off, wriggle a bit, and say,* "Ah, this feels so much better, and I can finally stretch out my big wings!" *Flap your arms like wings slowly.*

d. *Ask the children to close their eyes and listen.* Play some of the loud buzzing songs that the periodical Magicicadas will make from link: https://www.cicadamania.com/cicadas/cicada-songs-audio-sounds-noise/

e. Male cicadas have ribbed tymbals on their abdomen (place your hands on the tymbals on your sides just above your hips with your elbows turned outward). They use their muscles inside their body to bend their tymbals back and forth. When the timbal bends,

What do you call a Magicicada with no icada? Magic.

it makes a clicking sound. They bend it very rapidly to make their song. *Play the song.* https://www.cicadamania.com/cicadas/cicada-songs-audio-sounds-noise/

f.  *While standing up, arms on hips with your elbows turned outward, inhale and exhale as fast as you can, feeling your abdominal muscles. Ask kids to do the same, feeling their abdominal muscles.* One male cicada can sing for a long time. We are going to see how long you can all move your abdominal muscles like a male cicada. I am going to play another song clip, and I want you to keep pumping your abdominal muscles the whole time (It is tiring!). Link to song - https://www.cicadamania. com/cicadas/cicada-songs-audio-sounds-noise/

g. Female cicadas do not sing, but they communicate with wing flaps. *From a standing position, lift your arms up in a jumping jack position and then rapidly back down, smacking your thighs. Ask the kids to practice doing wing flaps.*

h. All together as a class, we are going to act like either a male or a female cicada. *Play their song one more time.* If you want to be a male cicada, hum in a deep voice and move your abdominal muscles rapidly. Those acting as female cicadas can lift your arms wide and smack the sides of your hips.

i. How does air come into our bodies when we breathe? Through our noses and mouths. Cicadas do not breathe like we do through our noses. They have holes along the sides of their bodies. *Point to the sides of your body in 3 places: below your armpits, mid -way between your hips and arms, and then to your hips.* These holes are called spiracles, and this is where they take in air to breathe. During the Cicada Olympics, you will look inside some exoskeletons and see tiny white threads. Those are the old spiracles.

j. Even with their big wings, cicadas are pretty bad at flying, which is why they're so easy for birds, dogs, cats and other animals to easily catch and eat. They might even fly into your head. They don't mean to; they're just very clumsy flyers. *If you have a big enough space, you can ask the kids to flap and move around the room - but they can not touch anyone else. Let them fly for about 20 seconds.* Was it easy to not hit anyone with your wings? It is hard for cicadas too.

k. We are so excited about the Cicada Olympics! Each of you will have your own cicada during the event. **Cicadas do not pinch or hurt people or animals.** It is OK to hold them, but you have to be very gentle with them so that you do not scare them. They only live for about one month, so let's help them have the best month ever.

You can follow up by decorating cicada houses in preparation for the big event. Link to this activity in Chapter 4.

## 9. Gather cicadas and exoskeletons prior to the event

### Advance Prep - Collecting Live Adult Cicadas

Determine where periodical cicadas will be emerging near you by checking the Brood maps here: https://www.cicadamania.com/cicadas/where-will-17-13-year-periodical-cicadas-emerge-next/ Collect live cicadas the day before the event. We recommend collecting **at least two cicadas per child** so you have a bunch of extras in case they choose to fly away. Pop-up insect habitats work well for containing cicadas. Many schools and families have pop up insect enclosures that they may have used to raise butterflies. Reach out to friends and families to borrow a few of these. You can also use large cardboard boxes, or clear bin covered with breathable mesh, but you'll need to cut a small door to reach into the box or bin so that the other cicadas do not fly away when the box is opened.

### Advance Prep - Collecting Exoskeletons

Exoskeletons are typically found around the base of trees where cicadas have emerged. Collectors will want to bring with them a big box, and fluffy materials such as rumpled t-shirts, cotton, or light weight blankets on which to gently set the fragile shells.

What do you call a cicada that spins in circles so rapidly that it knocks down trees and houses? A tornado cicada.

## How many exoskeletons will you need?

Example for a 65-participant event, including 3 school classrooms

| | |
|---|---|
| 5 | Exoskeletons at the Magnifying station |
| 300 | Constructing 3 exoskeleton pyramids, you'll need a hundred for each. |
| 85 | Spray painting shells for use as cicada gems (highly recommended). Collect at least one per child and 15 extras in case of breakage. |
| 175 | Guess the Number of Exoskeletons in the Jar |
| 565 | Total |

Why didn't the cicada mom recognize her son when he waved? Because she hadn't seen him in 17 years.

# Chapter 4

## Cicada Olympics Events - Thirteen Awesome Activities

# Make a Cicada House

## Objective

Construct a small house to transport individual cicadas to each event.

## Advance Prep

A few weeks in advance, order enough Chinese take-out food containers (8oz or 16 oz) so that each participant can have one. Companies such as Uline.com sell them in bundles. Plain white containers or brown containers with handles work well. Alternatively, you can use cafeteria milk or juice cartons that have been washed out well with soapy water. Opening up the full top of the pint size cartons works well, especially if you pop holes in advance on either side of the carton. Adults or children can slide a pipe cleaner through the holes to create a handle and hold it shut. Use a hole punch to add a few holes for insect breathing. Having children prepare their cicada houses in advance will allow them to focus on the other stations when they arrive at the event. Houses can be decorated if teachers choose to allow this.

- 1 Chinese take-out food container, carton, or tall yogurt cup per student
- 1 pipe cleaner to create a handle if using milk or juice cartons per student
- Hole punchers – to create breathing holes in the takeout containers and cartons
- Cicada House decorations if desired
  - o Construction paper, Scissors
  - o Glue
  - o Markers or colored stamps

## Station Instructions for Activity Leaders

Organize all materials on the table, such that a child can first pick up a container and fold it into the correct shape with the top flaps open. Using a hole punch, children should pop at least four or more breathing holes into the top and sides of their container. If there is no handle attached, help the children pop the correctly spaced holes on either side of the carton. Assist them if needed with sliding the pipe cleaner through the holes on the carton top to create a handle. Next, participants can use the markers and/or stamps to decorate their cicada house if desired. Practice opening and closing the top of the cicada house such that the child is confident that they can easily contain their cicada. When ready, students should move to the station where they can select their cicada.

Cindy Smith, PhD and Richard Groover, PhD

# CICADA OLYMPICS

## Pre-Collecting and Selecting Cicadas and Exoskeletons

### Objective
Collect enough live cicadas and exoskeletons to run an awesome event.

### Advance Prep - Collecting Live Adult Cicadas
Collect all live cicadas one day in advance. Collect two live cicadas per participant in case any fly away (which is their prerogative).

### Station Instructions for Activity Leaders - children select their live cicadas
When children arrive at this station, they should either have a cicada house or be ready to decorate a house. If their cicada house is ready for an occupant, ask the child to select a cicada from the butterfly habitat or box. Because cicadas are slow moving, children should be able to reach into the cicada enclosure and gently pick one up. For children that are nervous, remind them quietly by saying, *"Cicadas do not bite, they only suck plant juices. They are afraid of you. Hold your hands very still and I will place one into your hands, or you may pick one up to put into your house. Take a deep breath and move your hands slowly so you do not scare them. Whisper when you talk to them. Their feet will tickle your hands."* Have the child place the insect into the cicada house and then ask the child to name their cicada. Remind them that they will be releasing the cicadas or returning them to the enclosure after they have competed in the events.

What do you call a cicada with 1 wing? Grounded.

Cindy Smith, PhD and Richard Groover, PhD

## Cicada Boat Races

### Objective
To creatively design a boat that can be moved by wind and carry an adult cicada

### Advance Prep
Locate or borrow one or more shallow kiddie wading pools. Large plastic storage bins can be used, but a shallow hard plastic kiddie pool is preferred, as you can create more racing lanes. Divide the pool into three or more racing lanes and make sure each lane is at least 6 to 8 inches wide (15- 20 cm). Locate a water source and hose or buckets for filling the pool. Test the pool to make sure it holds water. Do not leave a full pool unattended. Rulers will be taped to pool edges. Strings will be attached to the rulers to create lane lines. A letter (see chapter 3) can be sent home to parents detailing the Cicada Boat Race Engineering Challenge rules. Students will create their own boat at home (or together in class ahead of time if possible) and bring it with them to the event.

### Materials
- Kids bring their boats to the event. Have a few extra boats on hand, in case a child does not have one or their boat tragically sinks.
- Kiddie pool or large storage bin that can be filled with water. Hose for filling pool.
- 3-6 Pieces of cardboard, about 8.5 x 11 that kids will use to fan the boats.
- Lane lines: 6-8 rulers and string for lane lines.
- Duct tape to secure rulers to pool edges.
- Clipboard with paper listing kids names, the place they finish if you plan to keep score.
- Pencils/pens for scorekeeper

Cindy Smith, PhD and Richard Groover, PhD

## Cicada Boat Race Engineering Challenge rules:

- All boats must be **8 inches long (20 cm) or shorter** and **no more than 4 inches (10cm) wide.**
- Boats can be built out of *any material* (sticks, leaves, wood, foil, plastic, paper, cardboard, water bottle, etc...). Boats will be moved by wind, so creating a sail-like structure to catch the wind is helpful.

- If you want to use an existing boat, such as a toy boat, **you must modify it in some way to make it your own creation** (Ex: turn it into a sailboat).
- To make sure your boat floats, test it at home before bringing it to the event.
- When the live cicada boat captain is placed in the boat, the crowd must be able to see him/her and the cicada must be able to move around the boat.

## Station Instructions for Activity Leaders

When children arrive at your station, ask them to get into lines behind each lane. If you have three lanes, then you have three lines. Explain the rules prior to each new race, "Boat owners, here are the rules. When I tell you to do so, you will step up to the race course. You will carefully, one at a time, place your live cicada boat captain in your vessel and gently set your boat in your lane. Next you will pick up the cardboard boat fan in front of your lane. When I count down and say 3, 2, 1 GO!, you will fan your boat until it reaches the opposite end. However, if your boat captain happens to fall out, you will gently move your boat back to the starting line and start again."

What do you call a cicada that is a good science teacher? A science communi-cada.

Cindy Smith, PhD and Richard Groover, PhD

## Cicada Car Races

### Objective
To observe an object's motion, and make predictions about speed and forces acting on the car (while cheering for their cicada to win).

### Advance Prep
Ask if your school, scout troop, or anyone in the neighborhood has any toy car ramps and toy cars you can borrow. Pinewood derby cars and tracks work very well, as do cars sized for preschoolers because cicadas will actually grip them. Cicadas tend to jump off of smaller hot wheels-sized cars, but if that is all you can locate, they are OK to use. A ramp can be created out of a long folding table where the legs on one end stay folded in and the other side is elevated or using slightly unrolled gym mats. A large piece of plywood can be used with long meter or yard sticks dividing the track in half. Ideally, having at least two lanes works well. The length of the ramp is not critical. It should be long enough to be exciting.

### Materials
- Ramps and cars supplied by the school or neighborhood
- Kids can bring cars in as an option
- Clipboard: paper with kids' names and space for the place they finished.
- Pencils for scorekeeper

### Station Instructions for Activity Leaders.
*you may want two leaders at this station*

Set the ramp(s) up in advance and test out the cars. When children arrive at your station, ask them to get into lines behind each of the two or more lanes. Share rules prior to each new race. You can use the following dialogue: "Drivers, here are the rules. When I tell you to do so, you will step up to the track. You will carefully, one at a time, place your cicada driver onto your vehicle and gently set the car in your lane. When I count down and say 3, 2, 1 GO!, you will let go of your car." The fastest car and driver wins. When a child shares why their car did not win, encourage them to tell you more. Ask them how they would reengineer their car to make it go faster.

Cindy Smith, PhD and Richard Groover, PhD

# CICADA OLYMPICS

## Measuring with Cicadas

### Objective
Provide practice with measuring using non-standard items.

### Advance Prep
Photocopy enough student worksheets for your event. To save paper, you can choose to laminate worksheets or put them in a slipcover and use dry erase markers so they can be reused.

### Materials
- 1-5 live cicadas in a clear container or cup and 3 exoskeletons in a bowl
- 6-10 common objects such as: a pencil, a pen, a marker, a stapler, a pencil cup, a big leaf, a small leaf, a stick, small toys, a cup, a sock, etc.
- Copies of the Measuring with Cicadas student worksheet, either enough for each child, or enough for each group when put into slipcovers or laminated
- Pencils or dry erase markers
- If outdoors, use rocks or heavy items to keep papers and objects from blowing away

### Station Instructions for Activity Leaders
Place a few live cicadas in a clear cup such that they cannot escape. Place your exoskeletons in a separate cup or dish and spread your objects out on the table. Place rocks or heavy objects on your stack of student worksheets.

When students approach your table ask them, "How long is your index finger in cicadas?" Show them how to gently hold a cicada and use it to measure their finger. "Well, it looks like your finger is about 2 cicadas long." Then tell them, "At this station, you are going to measure at least 5 objects in cicadas." Show them the worksheet and assist them with measuring. The challenge is that their cicadas may want to walk away, and kids may be so busy measuring that they forget to write down their responses. It's OK to help them out. Students may measure in live cicadas or exoskeletons

Cindy Smith, PhD and Richard Groover, PhD

## Measuring with Cicadas
## Student Worksheet

Write the name or draw the object you are measuring in the first blank. Write your measurement in the next blank.

1. The length of the _____ is _____ cicadas.

2. The length of the _____ is _____ cicadas.

3. The length of the _____ is _____ cicadas.

4. The length of the _____ is _____ cicadas.

5. The length of the _____ is _____ cicadas.

Which cicada won the exoskeleton beauty contest? No body.

Cindy Smith, PhD and Richard Groover, PhD

# Counting with Cicadas

## Objective

To integrate observed characteristics of cicadas and their life cycle into math problems.

## Advance Prep

Photocopy enough student worksheets for your event. To save paper, you can choose to laminate worksheets or put them in a slipcover and use dry erase markers so they can be wiped and reused.

## Materials

- Counting with Cicadas worksheets, one per child
- At least 1 to 3 adult cicadas in a clear cup
- Pencils
- Answer key for station leader

## Station Instructions for Activity Leaders

Place materials out at your stations. If children are bringing live cicadas to your station, you will direct them to observe their cicada to answer the questions. If they do not bring a cicada to your station, make sure you have a least one, preferably more to show them. As children arrive at your station, ask them, "How well do you know your cicada?" Let them know, "At this station we are going to carefully observe your cicada and write down some observations. Each question will get progressively more complex. Are you sure you know your cicada?" Help them count the legs on the first question, and encourage them to keep looking at their cicada as they do their calculations.

## Answer Key

1. 6 legs
2. 3 pairs
3. 3 x 6 legs = 18 legs
4. 2 red eyes
5. 10 red eyes
6. 5 friends x 3 cicadas = 15 cicadas x 2 red eyes = 30 red eyes
7. 60 + 72 =132 eggs
8. 16 – 4 = 12 could fly.

Cindy Smith, PhD and Richard Groover, PhD

## Counting with Cicadas
## Student Worksheet

1. How many legs does one cicada have? _____

2. How many pairs of legs does one cicada have? _____

3. How many total legs do 3 cicadas have? _____

4. How many red cicada eyes are there on one cicada?

5. If you have five cicadas in your container, how many red eyes will be looking at you?

6. If 5 of your friends each have 3 cicadas, how many red cicada eyes are there in your friend group?

7. If one female cicada laid 60 eggs and another laid 72 eggs in the same branch, how many total eggs are in that branch?

8. Sixteen cicada nymphs dug out from their holes in the ground and crawled up the same oak tree where they molted and climbed out of their old exoskeleton. Four of the 16 cicadas could not completely get their wings out of their old exoskeleton. How many cicadas could fly?

Cindy Smith, PhD and Richard Groover, PhD

# Cicadas Under Magnification

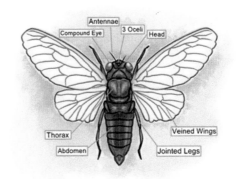

## Objective

To engage children in cicada anatomical discoveries and the connection of the functions of various insect body parts.

## Advance Prep

Locate four expired cicadas (you can put them in the freezer for a while), 2 males, 2 females, and two exoskeletons. Glue or use double-sided tape and attach each cicada or exoskeleton to a white index card, two of them facing up and two of them facing down. Attach one exoskeleton where the underside is visible and one exoskeleton with its back visible. These are your samples, which kids will magnify while you ask them to locate certain parts. Live cicadas also works well, but they may choose to walk away.

## Materials

- Magnifiers
- 4 Expired cicada specimens glued or taped (double-sided tape) to white index cards: Cicada adult showing the back side, Cicada adult showing the back side the underside, Cicada adult male, and a female, and 2 exoskeletons.
- Cicada Anatomy Worksheets -either 1 per student or just one laminated master

## Station Instructions for Activity Leaders

When students come to your station, let them know that they are going to get up close and personal with cicadas. If they are unclear, show them how to use the magnifier to zoom up on cicada body parts. Ask them to find the body parts detailed in the questions on the adult cicada under magnification student worksheet.

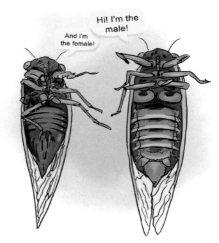

If you want to show the difference between males and females, remind the students that males have tymbals, on their abdomen, the organs from which they make their buzzing songs. Ask them to locate them.

Males also have a round abdomen tip, and females have a more pointed abdomen. If anyone asks, you can share that females use their ovipositors to dig gouges into soft branch tips to lay their eggs.

Cindy Smith, PhD and Richard Groover, PhD

45

## Adult Cicada under Magnification
## Student Worksheet

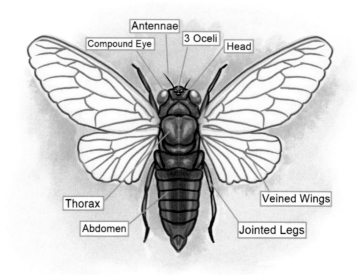

**Observations**

What color are the two eyes?

Can you find my 3 small dark eyes called Ocelli on the top of my head? _____
*These help me see predators coming from above.*

How many legs does your cicada have?

Circle what the mouth part or beak of a cicada looks like?   strong pinchers      a straw

Circle what cicadas do with this mouth part:   suck plant juice    pinch other bugs

How many dark lines do you see on each wing?_____
How many joints do you see the back legs? _____    Front legs? _____

Circle which pair of legs have the thickest segments?   Front    middle    back
*There are muscles in each leg segment, the biggest segments have the strongest muscles.*

Cindy Smith, PhD and Richard Groover, PhD

# Cicada Nymph Exoskeleton Under Magnification – Student Worksheet

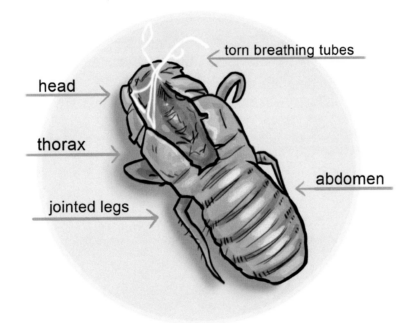

torn breathing tubes

head

thorax

abdomen

jointed legs

## Observations

Find the crack that runs down the back of the nymph. Look inside. What are 3 things you see?

*The crack is the opening where the adult cicada wiggled out (molted) of its exoskeleton.*

Can you find any small thin white strings inside the exoskeleton?

*These were the breathing tubes that connect to the sides of their body.*

Which pair of legs has the thickest leg segments? _____

*Cicada nymphs dig themselves out of the soil, so their front legs have the strong thick digging muscles.*

Find the wing pads on the back the thorax (they look like mini-wings). Are they large enough for this cicada nymph to fly?

Cindy Smith, PhD and Richard Groover, PhD

# Cicada Sketching
# Finish My Missing Half

## Objective
To practice careful observation, refine drawing and fine motor skills and recognize recognize bilateral symmetry in a two-dimensional figure.

## Advance Prep:
Print out one worksheet per student

## Materials
- Markers/colored pencils or crayons. Make sure to have red for eyes, orange for the wings and gray and black for the body.
- Some live cicadas for reference and inspiration

## Station Instructions for Activity Leaders
When students come to your station, let them know that they are going to practice sketching a cicada just like a real scientific illustrator. Humans, cicadas and other insects have bilateral symmetry, which means each half of their body looks like a mirror image of the opposite half. In contrast, flowers and sea stars have radial symmetry. Show students that they can count the number of squares to see how wide the head or the wing is so they know to draw the opposite side the same number of squares.

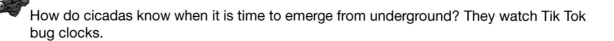

How do cicadas know when it is time to emerge from underground? They watch Tik Tok bug clocks.

Cindy Smith, PhD and Richard Groover, PhD

## Cicada Sketching
## Finish My Missing Half
## Student Worksheet

**Directions**

By counting the number of squares, finish drawing the mirror image of the cicada on the opposite side of the paper.

## 3D Cicadas

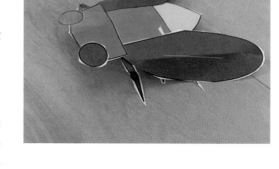

### Objective

To practice fine motor skills by cutting out body parts and assembling a 3D cicada.

### Advance Prep

Print out one template for each child. Decide whether or not each child will cut out the body parts and glue them together or, to expedite the activity, body pieces can be pre-cut in advance. Build a complete 3D cicada to display at this station during the event.

### Materials

- Printed templates for kids to cut, or pre-cut cicada body parts (head, eyes, body, wings, legs) for kids to glue
- Glue sticks
- Scissors, if parts are not pre-cut
- Finished 3D cicada model

### Station Instructions for Activity Leaders

When students come to your station, show them the completed 3-D cicada model. If body pieces are precut, instruct the child in the order in which to assemble them beginning with gluing the eyes onto the head.

The last step is folding the legs such that the cicada stands on all legs.

Cindy Smith, PhD and Richard Groover, PhD

## Build a 3D cicada -

Cut out each shape. Glue them together to create a 3D cicada. Bend the legs at the joints so it stands up. Fold the wings on the line so that they bend over the body.

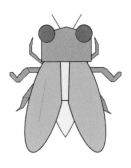

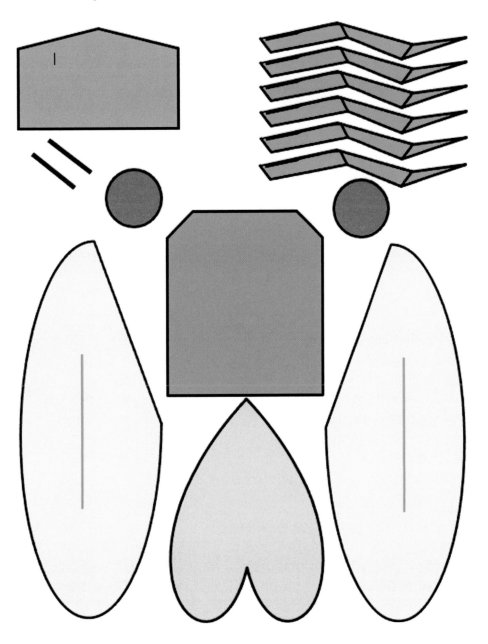

51

# Building Pyramids with Cicada Exoskeletons

## Objective

To gain confidence in touching insects and examining the texture, color and emptiness of cicada shells.

## Advance Prep:

Decide how many pyramids or exoskeleton sculptures you wish to create at your event. Each pyramid of sculpture will be constructed on a cardboard platform. This activity works well as a competitive event between classes, families or other groups. Collect a lot of exoskeletons in advance (you will need hundreds of them). Place the exoskeletons in a large pile or in a box on the table or station location. Using up-cycled cardboard, create a base for each pyramid. Create a sign for each team (for example, Mr. Rosa's Class, or the Martinez Family, 3rd Grade, etc) and a sign with directions: "Please glue exoskeletons to your team's (grade's, family's, etc) pyramid. How tall can you go?"

## Materials

- Platforms, at least 16in x 16in, made out of poster board or thick cardboard (one platform for each class or team)
- Glue (6 or more bottles)
- 100s of Exoskeletons. The more you have, the taller the pyramid (be sure to provide MANY exoskeletons)
- A printed sign designating which pyramid belongs to which teacher's class.
- A demonstration model – exoskeletons glued to make a pyramid or recognizable shape like a person, or a dog will encourage children's creativity.

## Station Instructions for Activity Leaders

An activity leader for this station is not required. Set out the platforms for the pyramids or sculptures. Label the platforms with the teacher's names or a sign. Glue a few cicada exoskeletons on each cardboard platform to indicate that the sculpture has been started. This is also a terrific event to have kids do at home if they have access to a lot of exoskeletons. The potential for incredible sculptures is unlimited.

Cindy Smith, PhD and Richard Groover, PhD

# Guess the Number of Cicada Exoskeletons in the Jar

## Objective

Estimating the number of objects in a container

## Objective

- Jar full of exoskeletons
- Small cards for kids to write their names and guesses
- Empty box with a slit cut into it for students to place their guesses
- Pencils
- Ruler in case students wish to measure the height or diameter of the jar.

## A few more jokes:

 Where do cicadas listen to music? Spotify.

 What do cicadas wear when they go to the beach? Sunscreen!

 What do you get when you cross a cicada with a sheep? A wooly screamer.

 What did the baby cicada say on the first day it emerged from the soil and saw the sky? Have I arrived?

Cindy Smith, PhD and Richard Groover, PhD

## Cicada Life Cycle

### Objective

Place the life cycle phases of the cicada in the appropriate place where they occur around a deciduous tree

### Advanced prep

Either sketch a large oak tree onto cardboard or print an image of an oak tree on paper and mount it onto cardboard. A tall, large tree is easiest to use. Print the life cycle phases onto cardstock, cut them out and laminate them. You may add velcro to the backs of the phases if desired so that kids can pull them off and reuse them again.

### Materials

- A cardboard cut-out or a laminated image of an oak tree. The bigger, the better.
- Circular cut-outs of the life cycle phases: tiny eggs, tiny nymphs, larger nymphs living underground, nymphs emerging from the ground, nymphs molting, and adults mating and egg laying

### Station Instructions for Activity Leaders

Set the tree up with the life cycle phases unattached. When children approach your station, ask them if their cicada is an adult or a nymph. Next, show them the different life cycle phases and ask them to place the adult up in the tree. Ask where they think a female will lay her eggs (on the tips of the branches). Where will the babies hatch? (on the tree branch). How might they get down to the ground? (they free fall, but they are so lightweight that they do not get hurt). Tell the children that the tiny nymphs dig into the ground to feed on small plant roots and hide from moles. Ask the children to place the rest of the phases on the board. They can use the tree cheat-sheet to see if they place the phases in the correct order .

Why didn't the cicada mom recognize her son when he waved? Because the last time she saw him he looked like an egg.

Cindy Smith, PhD and Richard Groover, PhD

# CICADA OLYMPICS

# CICADA OLYMPICS

Cut out the life cycle phases. Paste them on the tree in the locations where they occur.

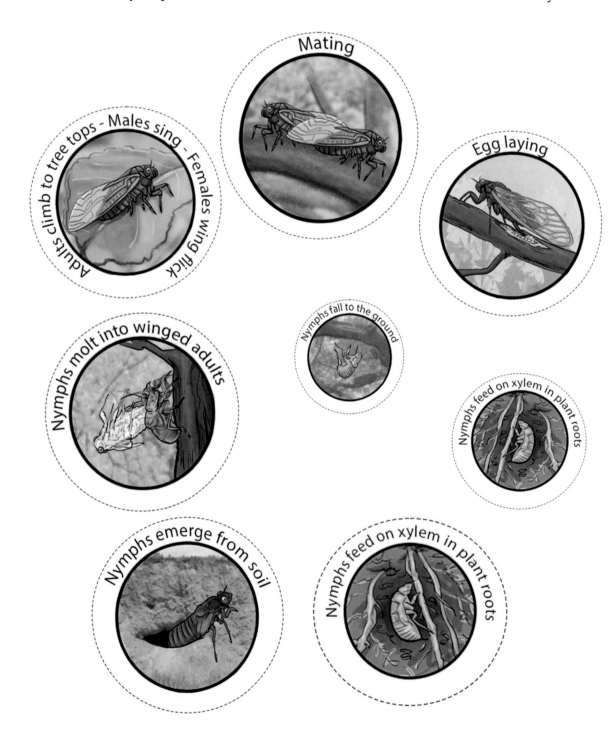

Mating

Egg laying

Adults climb to tree tops - Males sing - Females wing flick

Nymphs molt into winged adults

Nymphs fall to the ground

Nymphs feed on xylem in plant roots

Nymphs emerge from soil

Nymphs feed on xylem in plant roots

# CICADA OLYMPICS

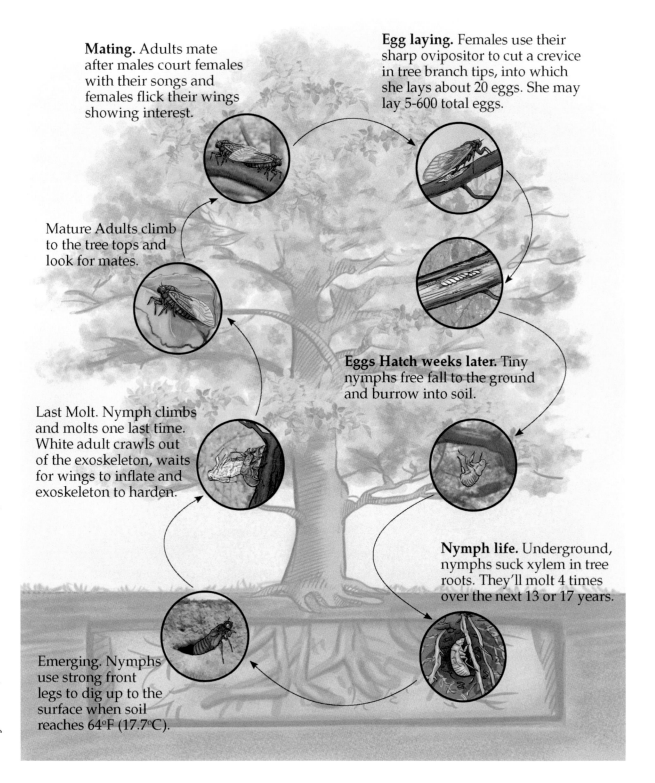

**Mating.** Adults mate after males court females with their songs and females flick their wings showing interest.

**Egg laying.** Females use their sharp ovipositor to cut a crevice in tree branch tips, into which she lays about 20 eggs. She may lay 5-600 total eggs.

Mature Adults climb to the tree tops and look for mates.

**Eggs Hatch weeks later.** Tiny nymphs free fall to the ground and burrow into soil.

Last Molt. Nymph climbs and molts one last time. White adult crawls out of the exoskeleton, waits for wings to inflate and exoskeleton to harden.

**Nymph life.** Underground, nymphs suck xylem in tree roots. They'll molt 4 times over the next 13 or 17 years.

Emerging. Nymphs use strong front legs to dig up to the surface when soil reaches 64°F (17.7°C).

Cindy Smith, PhD and Richard Groover, PhD

## Cicada Gems

### Objective
Provide shiny exoskeleton trinkets as a reminder of the Cicada Olympics event.

### Advanced prep
After collecting enough exoskeletons for this activity, spread them around outdoors on cardboard or newspaper. Using metallic, shiny spray paint (or other colors), spray all the exoskeletons. You have to rotate them to make sure you get all the crevices. Let them dry. Mount the shiny exoskeletons on small card stock that is printed with the word The Cicada Olympics.

### Materials
- Card stock of any color, printed with words - The Cicada Olympics and cut into small squares, about 2.5x2.5 inches. Pre-printed Index cards can be used as well
- At least one exoskeleton per child, more are recommended as they're fragile
- Metallic gold or silver spray paint
- Liquid glue to attach cicada to card stock
- For ease of printing, you can create a table with multiple squares into which you can print your event name.
- Print out enough cardstock pages such that they can be cut into squares so that all participants may receive a cicada gem as a reminder of the big event.

### Station Instructions for Activity Leaders
During the big event, carefully set out your metallic sprayed cicadas, your cards and your liquid glue. Use one blob of glue in the center of the card and then very carefully set the painted exoskeleton onto the glue. Let it dry before moving. Encourage children to be very careful when carrying their gem home as the shiny shells may crack.

Cindy Smith, PhD and Richard Groover, PhD

# Image and Video Gallery

https://www.drcindysmith.com/cicada-olympics

The best place to find out if there will be a cicada emergence near you is to check the brood maps located on this U.S. Forest Service Map or at these websites: https://cicadas.uconn.edu/broods/ https://www.cicadamania.com/cicadas/where-will-17-13-year-periodical-cicadas-emerge-next/

We highly encourage you to use the Cicada Safari app, to share cicada photos and locations: https://cicadasafari.org/

You can see images and listen to songs of annual and periodical cicadas on these sites: https://www.cicadamania.com/cicadas/common-cicadas-of-north-america/ and https://songsofinsects.com/cicadas

Eggs are tiny! You can see egg images here: https://www.cicadamania.com/cicadas/category/cicada-anatomy/eggs/

https://www.cicadamania.com/cicadas/where-will-17-13-year-periodical-cicadas-emerge-next/

At the time of this book publication, we find the website, cicadamania.com, which is maintained by leading cicada researchers, to be the most up to date resource with maps and reporting on emergence times. https://www.cicadamania.com/cicadas/where-will-17-13-year-periodical-cicadas-emerge-next/

# About the Authors

**Dr. Cindy Smith** is an award-winning educator, environmental scientist, and long-time cicada fanatic. She has dedicated her 25+ year career to making knotty ecological problems easier to understand and fun to study. She leads K12 and Community outreach efforts at George Mason University's Potomac Environmental Research and Education Center, where she translates complex research into eye-opening, engaging experiences. A talented and creative problem solver, working across multiple public and private stakeholders on environmental policy and programs. Her nature photography, wit, and wisdom consistently bring smiles to live and online audiences.

Instagram @cindywahoo
Twitter. @cindyloohoo9
Website: drcindysmith.com

**Dr. Richard Groover** is a retired college professor. He is a Fellow of the Virginia Academy of Science. He served on the Virginia Governor's Climate Commission from 2014-2015. He is currently on the Board of Trustees for the Science Museum of Virginia. He is the author of The Environmental Almanac of Virginia, 2nd edition and Environmental Cartoon for Teachers. He has a PhD in Environmental Science & Public Policy from George Mason University. His current science research activities include dragonflies and coyotes of Hanover County, VA.

In 2021, a special kind of cicada will emerge - the Brood X. This is the first time these cicadas will dig out of the soil in 17 years!

This book, by Cindy Smith, PhD and Richard Groover, PhD, will equip you with age appropriate information to make this a fun learning opportunity for your children. The authors have made the learning activities streamlined and easy to implement for individuals and groups.

Within these pages, you'll find:
- 13 fun cicada activities with instructions and materials list
- parent and volunteer information
- cicada jokes
- pictures
- online resources

**DR. RICHARD GROOVER** is a retired college professor. He is a Fellow of the Virginia Academy of Science. He served on the Virginia Governor's Climate Commission from 2014-2015. He is currently on the Board of Trustees for the Science Museum of Virginia. He is the author of *The Environmental Almanac of Virginia, 2nd edition* and *Environmental Cartoon for Teachers*. He has a PhD in Environmental Science & Public Policy from George Mason University. His current science research activities include dragonflies and coyotes of Hanover County, VA.

**DR. CINDY SMITH** is an award-winning educator, environmental scientist, and long-time cicada fanatic. She has dedicated her 25+ year career to making knotty ecological problems easier to understand and fun to study. She leads K12 and Community outreach efforts at George Mason University's Potomac Environmental Research and Education Center, where she translates complex research into eye-opening, engaging experiences. A talented and creative problem solver, working across multiple public and private stakeholders on environmental policy and programs. Her nature photography, wit, and wisdom consistently bring smiles to live and online audiences.

CICADA OLYMPICS

$14.9
ISBN 978-1-7370933-0-
5149
9 781737 093305